IF BUILDINGS COULD TALK

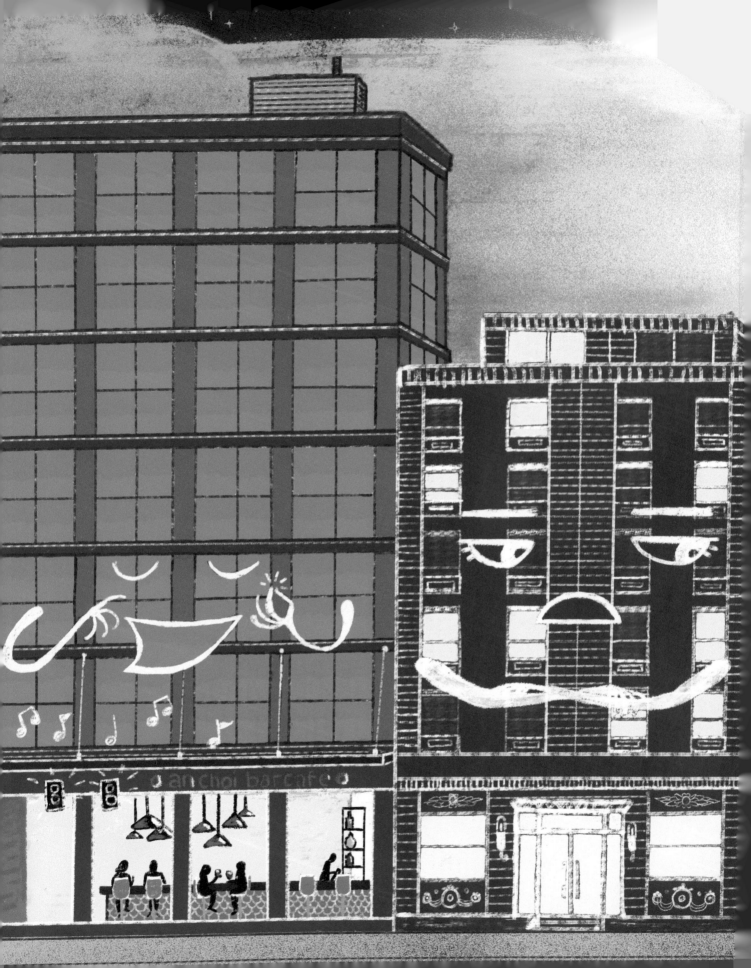

If buildings could talk, oh what would they say?

"I'm tired of holding your stuff all darn day."

Or maybe they'd talk of the things they've seen;

Like weddings, and birthdays, or days in between.

Do you ever guess what your house talks about?

Like the thoughts, and the feelings, it wants to get out?

Are they happy to see us?
Sad when we go?

Do they prefer spring, summer,
fall, or the snow?

Does it hurt when we stomp?
Do you need an ice pack?

"When you climb the stairs,
it's like scratching my back."

Or maybe your house is more like a friend,

That stands by your side through thick and through thin.

Protecting you daily from rain and from heat.

"My only request is you please wipe your feet."

All of these buildings for all different needs.

For shopping, or learning, or storing good reads.

There are buildings for ice cream and ones that save lives.

There are buildings for sleeping or checking your eyes.

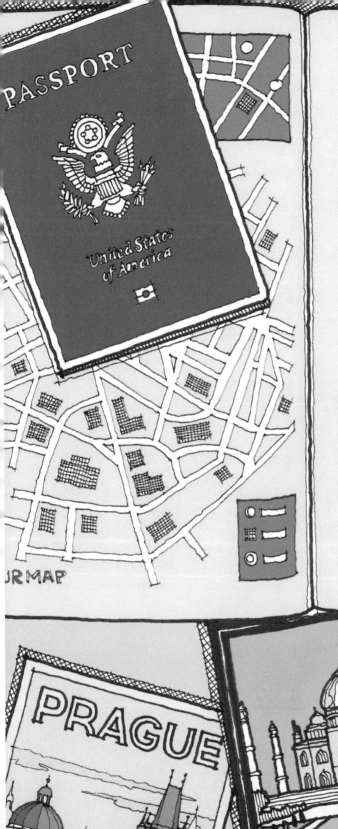

Some buildings are famous - celebrity status.

"People travel the world for a good look at us."

I'm certain you've heard a few names before...

"Pleased to meet you, I'm Taj, would you like a tour?"

ADMIT ONE
056 0418
056 0418

PRAGUE

INDIA

ATHENS
GREECE

Some buildings are average. You see them each day.

But that doesn't diminish the role that they play.

"I am a place where small businesses thrive.

Empowering the town to keep Main Street alive."

There are buildings so tall
that they scrape the sky.

"I've parted three-million-six
clouds passing by."

There are buildings so small
they fit only two.

"I'm the kiosk for finding
your way 'round the zoo."

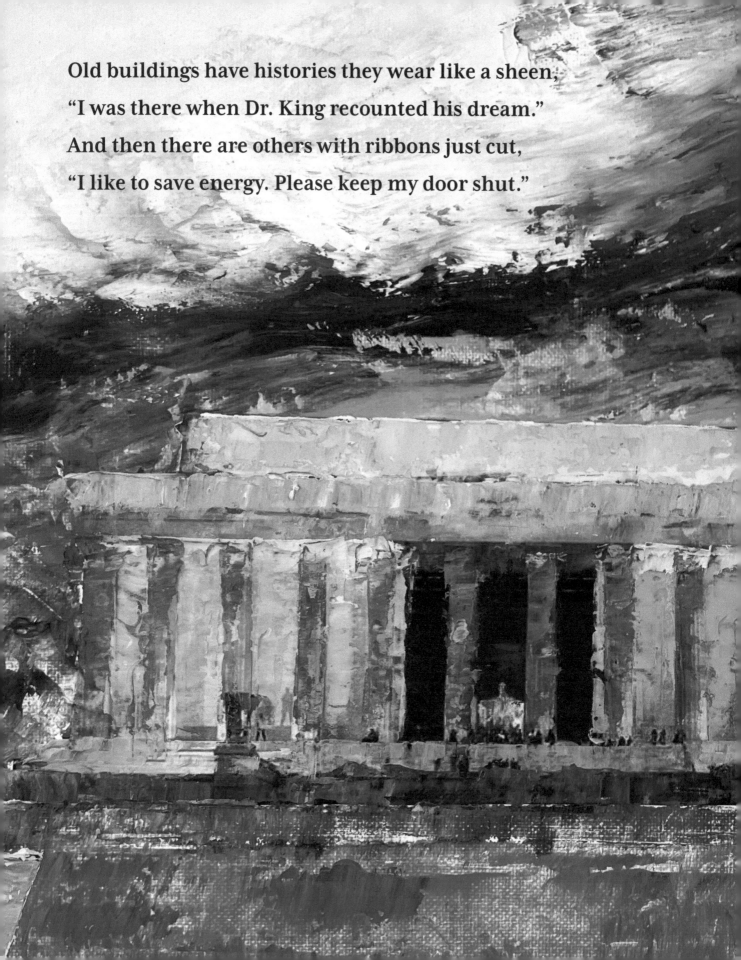

Old buildings have histories they wear like a sheen,
"I was there when Dr. King recounted his dream."
And then there are others with ribbons just cut,
"I like to save energy. Please keep my door shut."

Buildings are the backdrop of human existence.

Containing our memories and lending assistance.

They help us all, like our friends in wheelchairs.

"My ramps can be used
in place of the stairs."

I bet you have one in your
town with a story.

"You wouldn't believe what
I saw in my glory."

These buildings surround us
with more than good looks.

They've witnessed many things
not written in books.

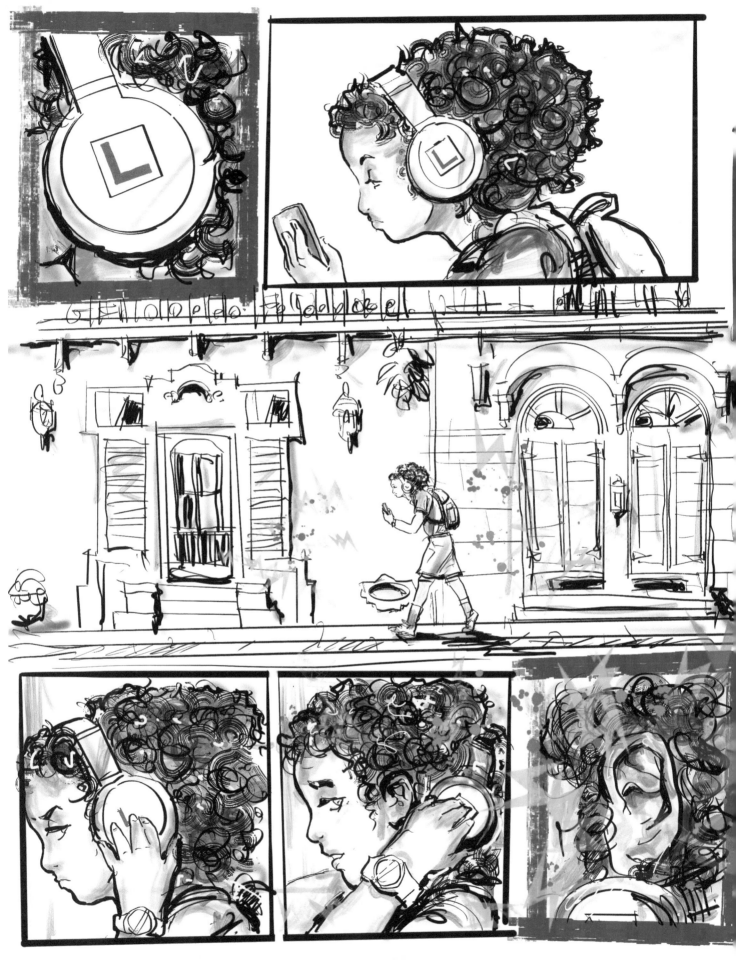

So, the next time you're out and looking around,
Don't be surprised if you hear a strange sound.
These buildings you see have a lot more to share.
They're willing to talk… if you're willing to care.

Now think of the buildings you use every day.
If they all had voices, what things would they say?

Use the following page to draw the stories
you think those buildings would tell!

AT LITTLE, WE BELIEVE THAT ARCHITECTURE HAS THE POWER TO TRANSFORM LIVES AND WE'RE EXCITED TO INSPIRE THE NEXT GENERATION OF DESIGNERS, ENGINEERS AND PLANNERS TO FALL IN LOVE WITH THE BUILT ENVIRONMENT.

AUTHOR: NIKKI CLINTON

Nikki is a designer, maker and writer living in San Clemente, CA. She has a degree in Visual Communications and has spent 15 years working in the architecture industry. A mother of two, she wanted to write a book prompting kids to consider their connection to the buildings in their world. And just maybe, pique their interest in the design industry.

COVER ARTIST: ELAINE O'BRIEN

Elaine is a designer whose life journey took her around the world before landing in the Carolinas. This adventure not only added colorful stamps in her passport but also embedded colorful stamps in her memories. Drawing from her life experiences, Elaine fuels curiosity in others through her imaginative imagery and graphics.

LAYOUT DESIGNER: CORY HESTER

Cory is a graphic designer who believes in working hard, having fun, and helping people elevate themselves and their ideas. Growing up around blue-collar work in Belmont, NC, he is committed to function and developing creative solutions that reveal their story and purpose.

ABOUT THE ARTISTS

Anh Tran is a spatial anthropologist and designer in Washington, DC. Specializing in visioning, strategy, analysis and design metrics, Anh has somehow made a career out of doodling on everything, everywhere, all of the time. She loves cities, people-watching, and speaking up - especially for good causes.

Darin Eng is a senior project manager in Newport Beach, CA. In addition to being a pragmatic problem solver for some of the biggest brands in retail, he is a designer at heart and loves to flex his creative left-brain muscle every chance he gets.

Becca Bellamy is a Charlotte-based interior designer fascinated by the way we interact with space. An accomplished artist, she enjoys exploring the contained space created by man-made structures, particularly the more uncelebrated places.

Devin Wiesler is an interior designer in Orlando, FL. A creative at heart, she fills her days designing and sketching all things minimalist, modern, and lovely.

Emma Wallace is an experienced graphic designer working in Durham, NC. With a background in branding, she has worked in many mediums – from logo creation and business papers to environmental design and everything in-between. Emma's passion is creating brands and seeing them evolve through various applications.

Charles Todd is a purpose-driven architect and father of five motivated to make a difference for future generations. Dedicated to excellence and the delivery of buildings, projects, and services, he serves as a Chief Operating Officer, a leader, a teacher, and a mentor in the community. Charles received his Bachelor of Architecture and Bachelor of Arts in Architecture from the University of North Carolina at Charlotte.

ABOUT THE ARTISTS

 **Thomas Carlson-Reddig (TCR)** has over 30 years of experience designing award-winning projects. His biggest passion lies in creating environments that help others be more successful. TCR carries a moleskin sketchbook wherever he goes - exploring design ideas and documenting the places he visits through sketches and watercolors.

 **Danielle Baker** is an interior designer with a passion for sustainable design, creative problem solving, visual communication, and bringing brand identity into three-dimensional spaces. A lifelong artist, she gravitated toward pen and ink drawing and watercolors as she grew up. Danielle believes that every project has a story and endeavors to tell those stories through the designs and art she creates.

 **John Komisin** remembers drawing a house for a 2nd-grade art project that helped him decide to become an architect. He started studying architecture in college over 50 years ago, so he's older than most of the buildings you see every day!

 **Ron Boozer** is an architect focused on improving the patient, family, and staff experience in healthcare design. As far back as the 5th-grade, he volunteered in children's hospitals to engage kids to have fun with art while enduring their difficult medical treatments. Currently, his mission is to work with project teams to inspire engagement, connection and community through art and architecture.

 **Jim Thompson** is a design addict, voracious reader, artist, collector, historian, teacher, father of three. When at his day job leading design at Little, Jim is at the crossroads of strategic thinking, research, education, and design and how this leads, informs and creates meaning in the built environment. In other words: do, say and make something that matters!

 **Aranya Mom** is an architect by day… and by night, but he pursues moments of escape through illustrations and art. Aranya works primarily in pencils, watercolor, and oil, and he is exploring new digital app-ventures with the Apple Pencil and iPad. As a child, he was shaped by comic books, manga, anime, fantasy and sci-fi. He continues in his quest to escape through art… it's what keeps him young at heart.

CPSIA information can be obtained
at www.ICGtesting.com
Printed in the USA
BVHW020436310522
638336BV00001BA/10